TASMANIAN MAMMALS

~*A Field Guide*~

Photographs & text by

Dave Watts

Pelican Press

Photographs by Dave Watts
Text compiled by Margaret Wood and Dave Watts
Design & typesetting by Lily Fox
Printed by Everbest, China

Revised edition ©2008 Dave Watts
Published by Pelican Press
PO Box 263 Kettering
Tasmania Australia 7155

ISBN 0 646143549

Front cover: top left to right: Tasmanian Devil, Common Wombat, Eastern Quoll (light phase). Main photo: Little Pygmy Possums

Inside front cover: Forester Kangaroos at Mt William National Park

Title page: Eastern Quoll (dark phase), Platypus diving

Inside rear cover: Tasmanian Devil at Mt William National Park

Rear cover: Spotted-tailed Quoll

To Helen

ACKNOWLEDGEMENTS

Many people have given freely of their time to advise on the text and to help ensure the accuracy of the information.

I am most grateful to David Rounsevell, Greg Hocking, Dr Steven Smith, Dr Sally Bryant, Nick Mooney, Jenni Burdon and Ingrid Albion for their continued support with this project and for their helpful suggestions for improvements to the original text. Many thanks also to Dr Robert Taylor for his help with the text and who together with Nick Savva gave expert advice on bat identification.

I was very fortunate in being able to accompany Menna Jones on some of her field trips in pursuit of carnivorous marsupials and she has greatly assisted with information on those species.

Many thanks go to Terry (Scobie) Pye and Geoff Copson for their help on rats and mice both native and introduced.

Many other people have given much valued help including Peter Brown, Graeme Challis, Mark Holdsworth, Steve Cronin, Roger Kirkwood, Tonia Cochran and Tom Mumbray who has kindly updated the map of reserved areas of Tasmania. David Pemberton was of great help in writing the text on the four seals included in this edition.

Many thanks also to Mike Jagoe of Talune Wildlife Park, Barbara Jones of Bonorong Park, Bob Reeves of the East Coast Bird Park and Andrew Kelly of Mole Creek Wildlife Park for allowing me access to their animals.

Much help has been received on photographic trips from Parks and Wildlife Service Ranger staff around the state, many thanks to them all.
Special thanks go to the Australian Antarctic Division for allowing me the opportunity to obtain the photograph of a Southern Elephant Seal at Davis Station, 'down south'.

Great support and encouragement has been given by Margaret Wood of the Environment Centre, Hobart. Without Margaret's help this project might not have happened as the idea for the book was originally hers.

My warmest thanks go to Helen Sargeant who has typed the text at all hours and who has greatly assisted on many photographic expeditions around Tasmania.

CONTENTS

FOREWORD 7

INTRODUCTION.. 8

HABITATS 10

MONOTREMES
Platypus 14
Echidna 16

MARSUPIALS

Carnivorous Marsupials
Spotted-tailed Quoll (Tiger Cat)........................... 20
Eastern Quoll (Native Cat) 22
Tasmanian Devil 24
Dusky Antechinus (Dusky Marsupial Mouse). ... 26
Swamp Antechinus (Little Marsupial Mouse) 28
White-footed Dunnart 30
Thylacine (Tasmanian Tiger).............................. 32

Bandicoots
Southern Brown Bandicoot 34
Eastern Barred Bandicoot 36

Wombats
Common Wombat 38

Possums
Common Ringtail Possum.................................. 40
Sugar Glider 42
Common Brushtail Possum 44
Eastern Pygmy-possum 46
Little Pygmy-possum... 48

Kangaroos and Wallabies
Long-nosed Potoroo.. 50
Tasmanian Bettong 52
Tasmanian Pademelon 54
Bennett's Wallaby (Red-necked Wallaby) 56
Forester Kangaroo (Eastern Grey Kangaroo) 58

PLACENTAL MAMMALS

Bats

Greater Long-eared Bat 62
Lesser Long-eared Bat 64
Gould's Wattled Bat 66
Chocolate Wattled Bat 68
Tasmanian Pipistrelle 70
King River Vespadelus 72
Little Forest Vespadelus 74
Large Forest Vespadelus 76

Mice and Rats

Water Rat 78
Long-tailed Mouse 80
New Holland Mouse 82
Broad-toothed Mouse 84
Swamp Rat 86

Seals

Australian Fur Seal 88
New Zealand Fur Seal 90
Southern Elephant Seal 92
Leopard Seal 94

INTRODUCED MICE, RATS & FOX

Black Rat 98
Brown Rat 100
House Mouse 102
European Fox 104

Appendix I
Footprint Chart 106
Appendix II
Where to See Tasmanian mammals 108
Appendix III
Bat Identification Chart 110

USEFUL ADDRESSES 111

GLOSSARY 112

BIBLIOGRAPHY 113

MAP 115

INDEX 116

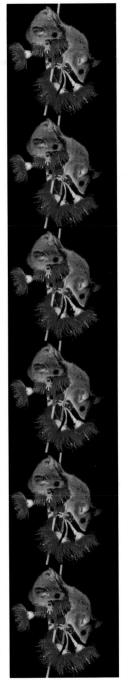

FOREWORD

Dave Watts has a rare talent for capturing the essence of the character of the wild animals that he photographs. His photographs are not only beautifully clear, showing the distinguishing features of the fauna, but many are exquisite. They are the product, of course, of countless patient hours waiting for just the right moment.

The immense value of this book is that it brings alive, in photographs and in text, the little known and the overall lesser known Tasmanian mammal fauna. Most Tasmanian mammals are nocturnal and cryptic in their habits and so are difficult for the non-specialist to experience. If you know where to look and what to look for, though, even the cryptic fauna or evidence of their passing is there before your eyes, and they are beautiful.

How many people wandering along a boardwalk in buttongrass moorland in a Tasmanian national park would recognise the feeding platform of a Broad-toothed Mouse? If you come across a half metre diameter patch of bare ground with rat-sized runways, well sat-upon stumps of worn-off buttongrass clumps, and tell-tale old whitened or fresh green rat scats, you know you have stumbled upon the nocturnal dinner table and resting place of this softly-plump herbivorous native mouse.

The photos do more than assist with identification. Dave's photographs of Eastern Quolls capture the exquisite spots, shell pink ears, soft fluffy tail, delicate paws and most of the all the light-footed dance of this species as it prances around foraging, always alert to sounds indicative of food or danger (in the form of devils). The Spotted-tailed Quoll photos encapsulate the strength and suppleness of this lithe arboreal predator, that can bound up tree trunks and come back down head first (even a domestic cat can't climb that well). The Bennett's Wallaby is also listening for predators (devils and eagles), its ears covering all directions, and the bettong appears ready to bound away at the slightest disturbance.

This pocket-sized book is just perfect for putting in the pack and taking with you into the bush. It will play a valuable role in making a cryptic fauna accessible to everyone. Increasing awareness of our unique fauna is invaluable when it is under threat from the criminal introduction of feral foxes to Tasmania and the Tasmanian Devil from a novel infectious facial cancer that is devastating populations. The synergy of these two events is most unfortunate. Devils are the top predator in Tasmania and have always been thought to play a role in aggressively suppressing foxes were they ever introduced. Devil populations in eastern Tasmania have now been reduced by up to 90% from this consistently fatal disease, leaving a food-rich, competitor-free environment in which foxes could thrive. The loss of devils as an ecologically functional species in Tasmanian landscapes is likely to result in ecosystem changes, including increases in macropod and possum prey species, increases in feral cats but also Spotted-tailed Quolls, and cascading effects on the ecosystem that could affect even vegetation communities. If foxes gain a hold, a number of mammal species for which Tasmania has been a fox-free refuge, are likely to disappear.

This is a wonderful and useful book that will be enjoyed by all ages.

Menna Jones, 7 May 2008

Opposite: Spotted-tailed Quoll

7

INTRODUCTION

Tasmania can rightly be called the "jewel in the Crown" of Australia when referring to its mammals. Many species of mammals, once widely distributed throughout southern Australia, have either disappeared or are sadly reduced to remnant populations. In Tasmania though, a combination of isolation (which until recently, has enabled the exclusion of such devastating introduced predators as the European Fox) and the rugged, mountainous terrain (which has slowed down the ever intruding process of land clearance) has enabled the great majority of native mammals to survive in healthy populations.

Predators like the Tasmanian Devil, once widespread on mainland Australia although having died out there many centuries ago, were until recently, common and thriving in Tasmania. Similarly the Eastern Barred Bandicoot which is now restricted to a few small colonies in Victoria, and terribly endangered there, can be regarded as common in many parts of Tasmania at least until recently. The sight of so many dead animals killed by vehicles on Tasmanian roads, whilst distressing, is an indication of the healthy state of the populations of many of our mammals.

Unfortunately, as already mentioned, Tasmania is now no longer Fox free. Recent evidence in the form of at least 3 road-killed Fox carcasses plus Fox prints and Fox scats has confirmed that a small population of wild Foxes now resides in Tasmania. These Foxes have almost certainly been deliberately introduced by a person or persons unknown. Recent evidence from the Australian mainland confirms that Foxes are responsible for serious predation on small to medium-sized native mammals as well as ground nesting birds, resulting in several species becoming extinct. If Foxes are able to proliferate in Tasmania then most of Tasmania's native land mammals will be at serious risk.

The objective of producing this volume is not simply to produce a picture book of Tasmanian mammals, but to help create an awareness of the animal treasures which coexist with us on this island. With very little effort it is possible to observe and enjoy the private lives of so many native species in their natural habitat.

This book brings together, for the first time, an outstanding series of colour photographs of all the native Tasmanian mammals including seals and the eight species of bats which are so often overlooked. The majority of photographs were taken especially for this book by Dave Watts. This involved many weeks of travel to the four corners of Tasmania and many hours of patiently waiting in the darkness. The results speak for themselves. Photographs taken by photographers other than Dave are credited where they appear.

This is essentially a guide to Tasmania's native land mammals and we have therefore not included the following introduced mammals; Fallow Deer, *Dama dama*, Hare, *Lepus capensis*, Rabbit, *Oryctolagus cuniculus* and Feral Cat, *Felis catus*. We have included three introduced small mammals, the Black Rat, Rattus rattus; Brown Rat, Rattus norvegicus and House Mouse, Mus musculus, as these can easily be confused with native rats and mice. In this edition we have also included the European Fox to encourage readers to report sightings.

In this revised edition we have included the two resident seals commonly found around the coast of Tasmania; Australian Fur Seal, Arctocephalus pusillus doriferus and New Zealand Fur Seal, *Arctocephalus forsteri*. Also the two rarer but regularly occurring Southern Elephant Seal, *Mirounga leonina* and Leopard Seal, *Hydrurga leptonyx*.

Tasmanian mammals are divided into three major groups, Monotremes, Marsupials and Eutherian or Placental mammals. Monotremes (Platypus and Echidna) differ from other mammals in that the females lay soft-shelled eggs and milk is supplied to the young after they hatch by means of numerous ducts opening into the skin of the abdomen, not via nipples. The name *mono* (one) t*reme* (hole) refers to the single body opening through which pass both faeces and urine. The female also lays her eggs through this opening but the male does have a separate penis.

Marsupials give birth to their young when they are very small and not fully developed. These tiny young crawl unaided through the fur to cling to a nipple, normally protected within a pouch, until fully formed. The name marsupial comes from a latin word meaning pouch. Most native Tasmanian mammals belong to this group.

Eutherian mammals include humans and most domestic animals. Young are carried inside the mother where they are fed and nourished by means of a placenta. They are born fully formed but require further feeding via the mother's nipples until they are large enough to become independent. The active rodents and the bats belong to this group.

All lengths and weights that have been used in this book are the average lengths and weights of mature animals except in the case of bats where a range of lengths and weights, and forearm measurements are given, as these measurements are vital for identification. It is the case with most of these mammals that the male is larger and heavier than the female.

Most Tasmanian native mammals are wholly protected under the National Parks and Wildlife Act (1970). Permits may be issued by the Parks and Wildlife Service for the trapping of animals for study purposes and also for the culling of some species which may be so numerous that they compete with humans or cause damage.

In this revised edition we have included a small distribution map of Tasmania for each species. The areas where the species occurs is shown by grey shading.

For taxonomic reasons some species have undergone a name change. The Broad-toothed Rat, *Mastacomys fuscus*, becomes Broad-toothed Mouse, *Pseudomys fuscus*. All three species of *Eptesicus* bats have become *Vespadelus*.

Our greatest concern must be about the continuing alteration and destruction of wildlife habitat outside the National Parks, through clearance for agriculture, drainage of wetlands, subdivision and the uncontrolled spread of urban sprawl. Certain forestry operations such as clearfelling and the woodchipping industry can have profound effects on wildlife by removing those old trees which contain hollows vital for many small marsupials and bats in particular.

The text of this guide has been designed to complement the photographs and will provide the reader with clear, easily-read information on identification, habits, habitat, distribution and status of the many mammals. This book is intended to be used as a reference guide to be kept in the car or carried in a rucksack. We hope that a greater awareness, interest and respect for our natural environment will ensure that the great variety of mammals to be seen on these pages will survive to be admired by future generations.

Dry sclerophyll forest

Manferns in rainforest

Buttongrass sedgelands near Melaleuca, Port Davey

Coastal heathland at Mt William National Park

11

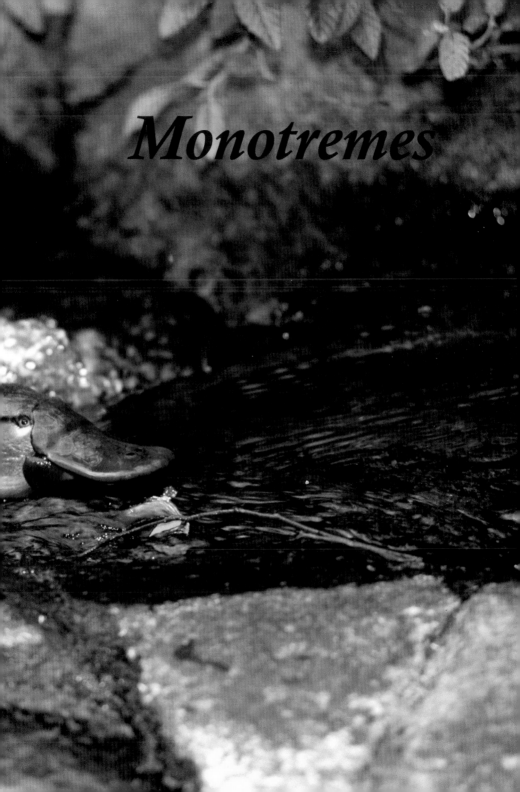

Monotremes

Platypus

Ornithorhynchus anatinus

Order MONOTREMATA   Family Ornithorhynchidae

Size		
	Head & body	43 cm
	Tail	12 cm
	Weight males	1. 7 kg
	Weight females	0.9 kg

Description: The Platypus can be distinguished from other swimming mammals (eg. Water Rat, see page 78) by its smooth action, low silhouette and absence of visible ears. The broad tail, webbed feet and duck-like bill of the Platypus are easily recognised when out of water. Its soft, dense fur is grey to brown on the back and creamy on the underside. The male has a venomous spur on each ankle and is capable of painfully wounding humans.

Habits: Aquatic. Most active in early morning and late afternoon. Forms a short burrow usually hidden under a tangle of tree roots just above the water line. Occasionally seen out of water.

Habitat: Freshwater lakes or rivers. Common in most Tasmanian river systems from sea-level to alpine areas as well as farm dams.

Food: Worms, insects, molluscs and small invertebrates. Food collected on the bottom is stored in large cheek pouches until the Platypus comes to the surface and consumes its catch.

Breeding: In October and November prior to egg laying, the female constructs an elaborate nesting burrow up to 20m in length. Usually two eggs are laid which hatch one to two weeks later. The young are fed on milk secreted through numerous ducts opening into the mother's abdomen. The young are weaned at four to five months.

Distribution: Tasmania, south eastern South Australia, Victoria, eastern New South Wales,
north and south eastern Queensland.

Status: Wholly protected by law. However dams, riverbank alteration, pollution and many other alterations to rivers reduce suitable habitat. When dams or culverts are placed on rivers and streams, Platypus avoid these and may then cross the road and be inadvertently killed by traffic. Common.

Echidna

Tachyglossus aculeatus

Order MONOTREMATA   Family Tachyglossidae
Size   Head & body   43 cm
       Weight   4 kg

Description: The Echidna has a long tubular snout, strong claws and reddish-brown to black fur. Protruding through the fur on the back are stout spines. Males have a spur on the ankle of each hind leg. The Tasmanian Echidna has more fur and less spines than the mainland form.

Habits: The Echidna usually prefers to forage in the early morning and late afternoon, though in cooler months it can be active during the day. When disturbed it may curl into a ball protected by its spines, or dig into the soil leaving only its spines exposed.

Habitat: Throughout Tasmania, but most often seen in drier areas.

Food: Ants, termites and other small invertebrates which it traps on its long tongue with sticky saliva.

Breeding: Late winter to spring. A soft-shelled egg is laid. The young hatches after about ten days, and is weaned after three months. The female may occupy a burrow while suckling her young, although generally Echidnas have no definite nest site.

Distribution: Tasmania and all mainland states.

Status: Wholly protected by law. The species is secure. Common.

Marsupials

Spotted-tailed Quoll
(Tiger Cat)

Dasyurus maculatus

Order POLYPROTODONTA   Family Dasyuridae
Size   Head & body males   60 cm
            Head & body females   40 cm
            Tail males   45 cm
            Tail females   37 cm
            Weight males   4 kg
            Weight females   2 kg

Description: Thick, coarse, golden-brown to dark-brown fur on the back with a lighter sandy-coloured fur underneath. Body and tail covered in white spots of different sizes. This is the main way of distinguishing this quoll from the Eastern Quoll (page 22), the latter having no spots on its tail.

Habits: Mainly nocturnal. Although an agile climber it spends most of its time on the forest floor and uses fallen trees extensively as runways. It generally appears slower moving than the Eastern Quoll.

Habitat: Favours the wetter forest areas of Western Tasmania, also dense coastal heathland and dry forest of north eastern Tasmania.

Food: Small birds, mammals, invertebrates and reptiles. Also scavenges carrion.

Breeding: Mates in winter, May to August, giving birth three weeks later. Litters of up to six young remain in the pouch for seven weeks when they are left in a den. Young are weaned by eighteen weeks. Dens in burrows, hollow logs and under rocks.

Distribution: Tasmania, southern and eastern Victoria, eastern New South Wales and eastern Queensland.

Status: Wholly protected. Land clearance and direct competition with foxes and feral cats are a threat to this species. Tasmanian population stable. Potentially vulnerable.

Eastern Quoll
(Native Cat)

Dasyurus viverrinus

Order POLYPROTODONTA   Family Dasyuridae

Size		
	Head & body	35 cm
	Tail	23 cm
	Weight males	1.3 kg
	Weight females	0.7 kg

Description: The Eastern Quoll occurs in two colour morphs. One being fawn to grey with white spots, the other less common morph is black with white spots. Unlike the former species it has no spots on its tail. The Eastern Quoll is considerably smaller than the Spotted-tailed Quoll and has comparatively larger ears and eyes.

Habits: Mainly nocturnal and less arboreal than the Spotted-tailed Quoll. It mostly hunts on the ground for its food. It is alert and quick, often dashing back and forth.

Habitat: Dry sclerophyll forest, rainforest, heathland, Buttongrass moorland and alpine areas. Also common in some agricultural areas.

Food: Mainly invertebrates particularly pasture pests, eg cockchafer and corbie grubs. Also small mammals, birds, fruit and sometimes carrion.

Breeding: Mates between mid May to early June, giving birth nineteen days later. Typical litter size is six. Young remain in pouch for eight to ten weeks. After this they are left in a grass-lined den in burrows, hollow logs or rock piles while the mother forages. The young are weaned by the end of December.

Distribution: Widespread in Tasmania. Some small populations may still exist in northern New South Wales.

Status: Wholly protected. Has successfully adapted to European settlement in Tasmania. Common at present but could be seriously threatened if Foxes proliferate. Numbers may increase following fire.

Tasmanian Devil

Sarcophilus harrisii

Order POLYPROTODONTA   Family Dasyuridae
Size   Head & body   60 cm
      Tail   24 cm
      Weight males   8 kg
      Weight females   6 kg

Description: A squat dog-like animal with large broad head and short thick tail. Coarse, thick black fur usually with irregular white markings on the neck, shoulders and rump. They have very powerful jaws giving them a fierce appearance.

Habits: The Devil is generally nocturnal. It runs with an awkward lope and leaves an easily recognisable track of one print, then two side by side, then one print (see page 105). They can frequently be heard growling and screaming when squabbling with others over a carcass. Young Devils are adept at climbing trees. During the day Devils shelter in caves, old burrows and thick scrub. Frequently follow roads, tracks and riverbanks, leaving a distinctive large scat (dropping).

Habitat: Forest, woodland and agricultural areas.

Food: Mainly a carrion eater, scavenging anything of animal origin. but also takes live prey. Diet includes wallabies, and possums or whatever else is available. Because of its powerful teeth and jaws, it can consume most of a carcass including the bones.

Breeding: Mates in March and gives birth in April three weeks later. Up to four young per litter. The young remain in the pouch for fifteen weeks and are completely weaned at about forty weeks.

Distribution: Tasmania. Once widespread on the mainland but died out many centuries ago.

Status: Wholly protected. Formerly common but recently the population has plummeted due to the fatal Devil Facial Tumour Disease (DFTD).

Dusky Antechinus
(Dusky Marsupial Mouse)

Antechinus swainsonii

Order POLYPROTODONTA   Family Dasyuridae
Size   Head & body   12 cm
            Tail   10 cm
            Weight males   65 g
            Weight females   45 g

Description: Soft and dense fur, deep brown-black on top and greyish white below. It has small eyes, small ears and long claws, and its muzzle is long and narrow.

Habits: Forages both by day and night. Moves in a jerky fashion and may be heard uttering a "siss" cry or a "chit" sound.

Habitat: Rainforest and wet sclerophyll woodland, particularly where there is dense leaf litter and an abundance of ferns.

Food: Soil invertebrates, fruit, lizards and carrion. Locates its prey principally by smell.

Breeding: Females construct grass-lined nests in creek banks or under logs and decaying vegetation. Mating occurs in early spring and all males die within three weeks of mating. The usual litter size is eight, with the young remaining in the pouch for up to eight weeks. The young are independent by about three months of age.

Distribution: Tasmania, Victoria and New South Wales.

Status: Wholly protected. Common within its forest habitat.

Swamp Antechinus
(Little Marsupial Mouse)

Antechinus minimus

Order POLYPROTODONTA   Family Dasyuridae
Size   Head & body   12 cm
          Tail   8 cm
          Weight   55 g

Description: Coarse and grizzled fur which has a reddish-grey tinge on top and greyish-yellow underneath. It has short ears, small eyes and long foreclaws. Its tail is covered with short hair.

Habits: Uses its long foreclaws to dig for food. Forages by day and night.

Habitat: Wet Button-grass sedgeland, but also found in coastal heathland and some wet flat drainage lines in north eastern and south eastern Tasmania. Also recorded from rainforest in north western Tasmania.

Food: Insects and larvae, lizards, earthworms and spiders.

Breeding: September to December. Normal litter size is six. As with the Dusky Antechinus, males die soon after their first mating.

Distribution: Tasmania, King and Flinders Island, south eastern South Australia and southern coastal areas of Victoria.

Status: Wholly protected. Threatened by destruction of its limited, preferred habitat, particularly by too frequent burning. Common.

White-footed Dunnart

Sminthopsis leucopus

Order POLYPROTODONTA   Family Dasyuridae
Size   Head & body   10 cm
        Tail length   7 cm
        Weight   28 g

Description: Dark-brown fur above and light-grey to white below. It has large round ears, a slender tail and white paws.

Habits: It is very quick moving and is mostly nocturnal.

Habitat: Widespread, but with patchy distribution in a range of habitats including rainforest, sclerophyll forest and heathland.

Food: Invertebrates, small reptiles.

Breeding: Nests appear to be in bark-lined hollows in trees and logs. Young are born in late spring and the maximum litter size is eight.

Distribution: Tasmania, Flinders Island, western Victoria, south eastern New South Wales.

Status: Wholly protected. Relatively little is known about the White-footed Dunnart because of the difficulty of capturing it. Potentially vulnerable.

Thylacine
(Tasmanian Tiger)

Thylacinus cynocephalus

Order POLYPROTODONTA	Family Thylacinidae
Size Head & body	120 cm
Tail	55 cm
Weight	20 kg

Description: The coarse fur is sandy brown in colour with dark brown stripes extending from the mid back to the base of the tail. It has a large head with a long muzzle and has a very wide gape. Its tail is semi rigid. Resembles a medium sized dog.

Habits: Mainly nocturnal but may bask in the sun in cold weather. Moves with a stiff gait. Emits a coughing yap when disturbed and a high pitched yip or yap when hunting. Very secretive.

Habitat: Once widespread, favouring sclerophyll forest and heathland.

Food: Kangaroos, wallabies and other game.

Breeding: In winter or spring. A litter of two or three young is carried in a backward-opening pouch.

Distribution: Tasmania. Once widespread on the Australian mainland, but died out many centuries ago.

Status: Wholly protected. The last documented Thylacine died in captivity in 1936. Since then many sightings have been reported and some people consider the Thylacine still exists. The decline of the Thylacine may be due to a disease which also afflicted the Tasmanian Devil and Eastern Quoll, and the bounty paid for every scalp the hunters produced. Officially classed as extinct but still remains wholly protected under the National Parks and Wildlife Act 1970. Unfortunately this unique creature is now almost certainly extinct.

Southern Brown Bandicoot

Isoodon obesulus

Order POLYPROTODONTA   Family Peramelidae
Size   Head & body   35 cm
        Tail length   12 cm
        Weight males   1.2 kg
        Weight females   700 g

Description: Dark, grizzled brown fur above, creamy white below. It has round ears, a long nose and a short pointed tail.

Habits: Nocturnal. Prefers to stay close to cover. Digs conical shaped holes in the ground when feeding.

Habitat: Widespread, but prefers scrub or areas of low ground cover which are burnt from time to time.

Food: Soil invertebrates, particularly earthworms and insects and their larvae.

Breeding: Constructs a well concealed nest of grass and other plant material, sometimes mixed with earth. Breeds between June and February. Litter size varies from one to four young which are raised in a rear-opening pouch. At least two litters are produced each season.

Distribution: Tasmania, Victoria, south eastern New South Wales, Northern Queensland, south eastern South Australia and southern West Australia.

Status: Wholly protected, while land clearance and the reduction in the frequency of small scale fires lessens the amount of suitable habitat. It is widely distributed in Tasmania, including agricultural regions. Still common in suitable habitat but would be seriously threatened if Foxes proliferate.

Eastern Barred Bandicoot

Perameles gunnii

Order POLYPROTODONTA   Family Peramelidae
Size   Head & body   32 cm
        Tail   8 cm
        Weight   950 g

Description: The fur of the Eastern Barred Bandicoot is soft and dense. It is grey on top with paler bands across the rump and is a lighter grey underneath. It has big ears, a white tail and long claws on its forefeet. The snout is very pointy.

Habits: Mostly nocturnal. It moves at a rapid gallop or bound, and can clear over one metre at a leap. Digs conical shaped holes in the ground when feeding.

Habitat: Prefers open grasslands with nearby scrub or woodland. Now occurs mainly amongst agricultural areas.

Food: Soil invertebrates, including pasture pests e.g. cockchafer and corbie grubs. It also eats berries in season.

Breeding: Late May through to March. Litter size is one to four, raised in a rear-opening pouch. Young animals are independent three to five months after birth.

Distribution: Tasmania and south western Victoria where a few small colonies have been established.

Status: Wholly protected. It has adapted well to European settlement in Tasmania but has almost died out on the Australian mainland. Remains common although vulnerable in Tasmania. Would be seriously threatened if Foxes proliferate.

Common Wombat

Vombatus ursinus

Order DIPROTODONTA   Family Vombatidae
Size   Head & body   100 cm
    Tail   2.5 cm
    Weight   26 kg

Description: Coarse, dark brown fur. Solid and powerfully built body. Short legs with broad paws and strong claws. Short ears, small eyes and a large naked nose.

Habits: Largely nocturnal but in cold weather may be seen grazing or basking in the sun. Dung is easily recognisable, being rectangular and usually deposited on rocks or logs.

Habitat: Widespread from sea level to alpine areas. Heathland and forest on sandy soil is preferred.

Food: Native grasses, herbs, shrubs and succulent roots.

Breeding: Constructs elaborate burrows up to 20m long with interconnecting tunnels. Breeding occurs at any time of the year but usually in winter. Generally one young is born, remaining in the pouch for six months, then staying with the mother until it is about eighteen months old.

Distribution: Tasmania, south eastern South Australia, Victoria and New South Wales.

Status: Partly protected. The species is secure at present, although suffering a reduction of range through clearing for agriculture. Common in suitable habitat, particularly the north east.

Common Ringtail Possum

Pseudocheirus peregrinus

Order DIPROTODONTA   Family Petauridae
Size   Head & body   33 cm
         Tail   33 cm
         Weight   950 g

Description: Reddish brown to dark-grey fur above; lighter below. Short ears with a white patch behind. Distinguished from the Brushtail Possum (page 44), by its tapering, white-tipped tail and light ears.

Habits: Nocturnal. A vocal animal with a soft, high-pitched twittering call. An arboreal species which builds a spherical nest of bark lined with grass in trees.

Habitat: Widespread throughout Tasmania. Most abundant in areas of tall dense Tea-Tree.

Food: Leaves, flowers (particularly eucalypts) and fruit.

Breeding: Builds a spherical, bark or grass-lined nest in hollows, forks of trees and amongst branches. Breeding occurs from April to November with two young usually born. These remain in the pouch for four months and are fully weaned at six months. Once out of the pouch, the young may be carried on the mother's back while she forages.

Distribution: Tasmania, south eastern South Australia, Victoria, New South Wales, Queensland and south west Western Australia.

Status: Wholly protected. Numbers declined during the 1950's but have since recovered.

Sugar Glider

Petaurus breviceps

Order DIPROTODONTA   Family Petauridae
Size   Head & body   17 cm
       Tail   19 cm
       Weight   120 g

Description: Soft, dense, blue-grey coloured fur with a dark stripe down the centre of its back. Bushy tail sometimes tipped with white. A flap of loose skin extends along the side of the body from front paw to back paw which allows the animal to glide for a distance of up to 50m from the tallest trees.

Habits: Nocturnal and arboreal. The Sugar Glider has a range of calls, a shrill yapping to warn of danger, a scream when fighting and a defiant chatter when disturbed. In very cold weather it may conserve energy by huddling with others in a nest hollow or by becoming torpid. Lives in groups with up to seven adults and their young sharing a nest.

Habitat: Open forest and woodland areas.

Food: Invertebrates, flowers, nectar and gum produced by acacias and eucalypts.

Breeding: Constructs a leaf-lined nest in hollows of old trees. Breeding begins in August. Usual litter size is two and these remain in the pouch for two to three months, then spend another month in the group nest.

Distribution: Tasmania and all mainland states. Absent from much of the west and central mainland. Probably introduced into Tasmania.

Status: Wholly protected. Species seems secure at present, but may undergo a reduction in numbers with clearfelling and removal of old nesting trees with hollows.

Common Brushtail Possum

Trichosurus vulpecular

Order DIPROTODONTA   Family Phalangeridae
Size   Head & body   45 cm
        Tail   30 cm
        Weight   3.5 kg

Description: The Brushtail Possum has very thick soft fur ranging in colour from silver-grey to black, to reddish and sometimes golden. It has long oval ears and a bushy tail with a naked area along the end which distinguishes it from the Ringtail Possum (Page 40) which has a tapering white-tipped tail.

Habits: Nocturnal. Utters sharp hisses or deep guttural coughs, particularly in the breeding season. Feeds on the ground and in trees but is less arboreal in Tasmania compared with mainland Australia.

Habitat: Sclerophyll forests and woodland, also agricultural and suburban areas. Absent from areas of extensive rainforest and sedgeland.

Food: In dry forests - grasses, herbs, acacias and eucalypt leaves. In wet forest - ferns, grasses and Myrtle leaves.

Breeding: Between March and June with a secondary breeding period between August and October. A single young is born, and remains in the pouch for up to six months. A further two months are spent riding on the mother's back prior to gaining independence.

Distribution: Tasmania, and all mainland states.

Status: Partly protected species which has generally benefited from some agricultural and forestry practices. Abundant in most areas.

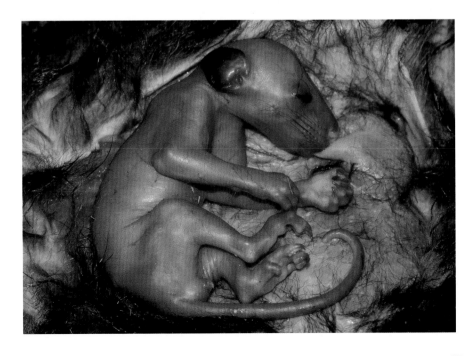

Eastern Pygmy-possum

Cercartetus nanus

Order DlPROTODONTA		Family Burramyidae
Size	Head & body	9 cm
	Tail	9 cm
	Weight	30 g

Description: Fur is pale fawn-grey above and lighter coloured below. Prehensile tail which is naked for most of the length. It has oval shaped ears and pinkish feet and nose.

Habits: Nocturnal. It is an agile climber. In winter when food is short much of its time is spent in a state of torpor. Torpor may last for two weeks at a time.

Habitat: Primarily wet forests and rainforest including sclerophyll woodland.

Food: Insects, spiders and small lizards, also nectar and pollen from banksias, bottlebrushes and eucalypts gathered with the brush-tipped tongue.

Breeding: Nests lined with shredded bark are constructed in very small tree holes or in tree forks. Breeds late winter to spring and up to five young remain in the pouch for about six weeks.

Distribution: Tasmania, Victoria, eastern New South Wales and south eastern Queensland.

Status: Wholly protected. Threatened by clearfelling of old growth mature forest which contains nesting hollows. Widespread and apparently secure.

Little Pygmy-possum

Cercartetus lepidus

Order DIPROTODONTA   Family Burramyidae

Size   Head & body   6 cm
           Tail   7 cm
           Weight   7 g

Description: Soft pale fawn-coloured fur above, light-grey below. Large ears and eyes and a prehensile tail.

Habits: Nocturnal. Like the Eastern Pygmy-possum, it undergoes periods of torpidity, particularly in winter when food is scarce. Spends most of its time close to the ground or in dense scrub to avoid attacks from owls.

Habitat: All forest types except rainforest; favours dry sclerophyll forest.

Food: Insects, spiders and small lizards; probably also nectar, blossoms and fruit.

Breeding: Builds bark-lined nests, usually in small hollows in trees. Young are born between September and January with up to four per litter. After about six weeks the young are too big for the pouch and may either be left in the nest while the mother forages, or travel clinging to her fur. Young become independent at about three months.

Distribution: Tasmania, Victoria, South Australia, Kangaroo and Flinders Islands.

Status: Wholly protected. Extensive clearing of sclerophyll forests lessens the available habitat. Forests regenerated after clearfelling are unlikely to provide suitable nesting sites. Widespread, although potentially vulnerable.

Long-nosed Potoroo

Potorous tridactylus

Order DIPROTODONTA   Family Potoroidae
Size   Head & body   36 cm
          Tail   23 cm
          Weight   1.3 kg

Description: This small wallaby has red-brown to grey coloured fur above and paler below. Long tapering nose with bare patch of skin above the nostrils. Short rounded ears. Some have a white tip to their relatively short tail.

Habits: Mostly nocturnal but may be seen at dusk. When moving quickly it hops on its hind legs.

Habitat: Widespread in most forest types and heathland which provides thick ground cover through which the Potoroo forms a network of runways. Prefers areas with light sandy soil.

Food: Mainly underground fungi; also soil invertebrates and tubers.

Breeding: Has two breeding seasons in winter/early spring and late summer. A single young is produced at a time and remains in the pouch for four months.

Distribution: Tasmania, Victoria, New South Wales, King and Flinders Islands. Tasmanian subspecies in Tasmania, Bass Strait Islands.

Status: Wholly protected. Much habitat has been reduced by land clearing. Still common in areas of remaining habitat although potentially vulnerable. Would be seriously threatened if Foxes proliferate.

Tasmanian Bettong

Bettongia gaimardi

Order DIPROTODONTA   Family Potoroidae
Size   Head & body   32 cm
    Tail   32 cm
    Weight   2 kg

Description: Coarse brownish-grey coloured fur above; greyish-white underneath. Short round ears and long tail which usually has a white tip.

Habits: Nocturnal. Individuals sometimes travel over a kilometre from the nest to a feeding area.

Habitat: Widespread but patchily distributed in eastern Tasmania in dry sclerophyll forest and woodland with an open understorey. Most abundant where soils are low in nutrients.

Food: The bulk of the bettong's diet is the fruiting bodies of underground fungi. Also eats seeds, mushrooms, insects and gum from acacia shrubs. Fire often causes fruiting bodies to increase so allowing bettong reproduction to increase.

Breeding: Builds a woven nest of dry grass and bark in a hollow under a fallen tree or among bushes. Material for the nest construction is carried in the bettong's tightly coiled tail. Breeding occurs all year round. Females give birth to one young at a time and may produce two to three per year. The young are usually in the pouch for about three and a half months and are weaned at six months.

Distribution: Tasmania.

Status: Wholly protected. Young regenerated forests produced following clearfelling are unsuitable for Tasmanian Bettongs and large areas of habitat are being lost. The few remaining high density populations are on private land. Still common within its declining restricted habitat although potentially vulnerable. Would be seriously threatened if Foxes proliferate.

Tasmanian Pademelon
(Rufous Wallaby or Red-bellied Pademelon)

Thylogale billardierii

Order DIPROTODONTA   Family Macropodidae
Size   Head & body   60 cm
        Tail   41 cm
        Weight males   7 kg
        Weight females 4 kg

Description: The dense fur is dark-brown or grey-brown above and reddish-brown underneath. Males are much larger than females and are considerably more muscular in forearms and chest.

Habits: Nocturnal.

Habitat: Widespread in all areas where there is dense undergrowth, preferring forest adjacent to cleared areas for feeding. Shelters in dense vegetation during the day.

Food: Grasses, herbs and taller shrubs.

Breeding: Breeding is continuous, but most of the young are born in early winter with another smaller peak in early summer. One young is born and remains in the pouch for six months.

Distribution: Tasmania.

Status: Partly protected. Large numbers apparent in forestry and agricultural areas. This species once occurred on the mainland but now appears to have died out. Abundant at present but could become rare if Foxes proliferate.

Bennett's Wallaby
(Red-necked Wallaby)

Macropus rufogriseus

Order DIPROTODONTA   Family Macropodidae
Size   Head & body   80 cm
        Tail   75 cm
        Weight males   15 kg
        Weight females   11 kg

Description: Soft thick fur, dark grey above and paler below except on the neck where it is reddish-brown. Black nose and paws.

Habits: Mostly nocturnal but can be seen at dusk. Usually solitary, although they may feed close to each other.

Habitat: Widespread throughout Tasmania in open forests, heathland and sedgeland, particularly in areas adjacent to pasture. Rests during the day among dense patches of scrub.

Food: Grasses and herbs.

Breeding: Young are born between January and July with most females giving birth in late summer. One young is born and remains in the pouch for nine months. Weaning is about seventeen months.

Distribution: Tasmania, Victoria, south eastern South Australia, eastern New South Wales, south eastern Queensland, King and Flinders Islands.

Status: Partly protected. The species appears to have benefited from European settlement with large numbers in forestry and agricultural areas. Abundant.

Forester Kangaroo
(Eastern Grey Kangaroo)

Macropus giganteus

Order DIPROTODONTA   Family Macropodidae
Size   Head & body   150 cm
        Tail   94 cm
        Weight males   50 kg
        Weight females 25 kg

Description: The Forester Kangaroo has soft, brownish-grey fur above and paler coloured fur underneath. It has a hairy muzzle with fine hairs between the nostrils and upper lip. Relatively large ears.

Habits: Active in the evenings and at night. May be heard making a series of clucking sounds, or if alarmed a guttural cough. Unlike other Tasmanian macropods the Forester Kangaroo forms social groups or mobs.

Habitat: It is the only kangaroo occurring in Tasmania, and is found in dry sclerophyll forests, woodlands and open grassy plains in the north east and the Midlands. The species has been introduced to Maria Island National Park.

Food: Grasses.

Breeding: Mainly in summer with one young born. Young stays in pouch for ten months and is weaned at about eighteen months, by which time the mother may have another young in the pouch as with most other kangaroos and wallabies.

Distribution: Tasmania, Victoria, New South Wales, eastern South Australia and Queensland.

Status: Wholly protected. Populations were greatly depleted by hunting and the extensive agricultural development of the Tasmanian Midlands. Active measures are being taken to ensure the continued survival of the species in Tasmania. Common in a few selected areas.

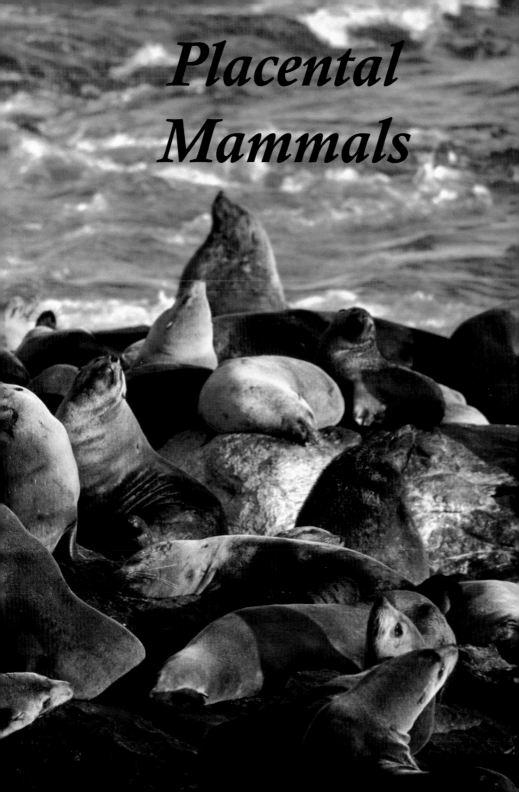

Placental Mammals

Greater Long-eared Bat

Nyctophilus timoriensis

Order CHIROPTERA   Family Vespertilionidae
Size   Head & body   65 mm
       Tail   50 mm
       Forearm   43.5- 48.0 mm
       Weight   9.8-18.9 g

Description: Dark brown fur above; lighter brown below. Ears large and joined over the head.

Habits: Nocturnal. Hibernates from late autumn to early spring.

Habitat: A wide range of forest habitats, where it roosts in trees during the day, often with others of the same species.

Food: Insects, mostly non-flying ones which are collected off vegetation and from the forest floor. It feeds by flying slowly close to the ground and amongst the undergrowth.

Breeding: One or two young are born in late spring or early summer and are weaned by mid-summer.

Distribution: Tasmania, Victoria, New South Wales, Queensland, South Australia and Western Australia.

Status: Wholly protected. Forests regenerated after logging operations are unlikely to provide as many suitable roosting sites as mature forest. In the long term a decline in this species may result. Uncommon. This bat species was previously named *N. gouldii*.

63

Lesser Long-eared Bat

Nyctophilus geoffroyi

Order CHIROPTERA   Family Vespertilionidae

Size	Head & body	40- 50 mm
	Tail	43 mm
	Forearm	36.5-42.6 mm
	Weight	6.8-12.2 g

Description: Light grey-brown fur above and pale below. Ears are very long and are joined above the forehead. May be distinguished from the Greater Long-eared Bat by its smaller size, paler fur and by its well developed Y-shaped nose leaf.

Habits: Nocturnal. Hibernates from late autumn to early spring.

Habitats: Widespread in all forest types, including the South West. It roosts in trees, often with others of the same species. This species has also been recorded foraging and roosting in towns.

Food: Insects, mostly flying ones. It feeds by flying slowly close to the ground, sometimes alighting in the undergrowth.

Breeding: Young are born late spring or early summer, with a usual litter size of two. Young are weaned by mid-summer.

Distribution: All mainland states and Tasmania.

Status: Wholly protected. Forests regenerated after clearfelling operations are unlikely to provide as many suitable roost sites as mature forests, therefore a long-term decline in the species is likely. Common at present.

Gould's Wattled Bat

Chalinolobus gouldii

Order CH1ROPTERA   Family Vespertilionidae
Size   Head & body   65-75(70) mm
        Tail   40-50(45) mm
        Forearm   44.0-48.7 mm
        Weight   12.2-17.8 g

Description: Fur on the dorsal surface is dark brown tending to black on the head and shoulders; slightly paler fur underneath. Fleshy lobes at the base of the ear and corner of the mouth. It has an elevated forehead.

Habits: Nocturnal. Roosts in hollow trees, usually in colonies. Hibernates from late autumn to early spring.

Habitat: A wide range of forest types, although not recorded in South-West Tasmania.

Food: Insects. Feeds by flying quickly either in upper layers of forest canopy or above it.

Breeding: Young are born in late spring or early summer with litter size usually two. The young attach themselves to the nipples and remain attached while the mother is flying. Weaning is completed by early February.

Distribution: Tasmania and all mainland states.

Status: Wholly protected. Forests regenerated after logging operations are unlikely to provide as many suitable roosting sites as mature forests. In the long term a decline in the species may result. Uncommon.

Chocolate Wattled Bat

Chalinolobus morio

Order CHIROPTERA   Family Vespertilionidae
Size   Head & body   50-60(57) mm
          Tail   45-50(48) mm
          Forearm   36.2-43 mm
          Weight   6.7-13.7 g

Description: Chocolate-brown coloured fur all over. Ear lobes are not as conspicuous as that of the Gould's Wattled Bat.

Habits: Nocturnal. Hibernates in the winter but its period of hibernation is shorter than the other species of Tasmanian bats. Usually roosts in trees, often communally.

Habitat: All forest types including rainforest.

Food: Insects collected mostly in the middle layers of the forest between the canopy and understorey.

Breeding: Young are born in late spring and early summer with usually one young per litter. Weaning is complete in February, usually later than other species.

Distribution: Tasmania and all mainland states.

Status: Wholly protected. However, forests regenerated after logging operations are unlikely to provide as many suitable roosting sites as mature forests. This may result in a long-term decline of the species. Common.

Tasmanian Pipistrelle

Falsistrellus tasmaniensis

Order CHIROPTERA
Family Vespertilionidae
Size   Head & body   65 mm
        Tail   40 mm
        Forearm   46-52.2 mm
        Weight   16.2-24.1 g

Description: Reddish-brown fur above and a paler brown on the belly. Ears are long and pointed with a notch at the top. It is the largest bat found in Tasmania.

Habits: Nocturnal. Hibernates from late autumn to early spring. Roosts in trees, often communally. Flies fast and direct.

Habitat: Most forest types, but has also been found foraging and roosting in urban environments.

Food: Insects; mainly beetles. Feeds in upper layers of forest canopy or above it.

Breeding: A single young is born in late spring or early summer. Weaning is completed by early February.

Distribution: Tasmania, Victoria, New South Wales, south eastern Queensland and south western West Australia.

Status: Wholly protected. However, forests regenerated after logging operations are unlikely to provide as many suitable roosting sites as mature forests. This may result in a long-term decline of this species. Uncommon.

King River Vespadelus
(Formerly Eptesicus)

Vespadelus regulus

Order CHIROPTERA   Family Vespertilionidae
Size   Head & body   45-55(47) mm
          Tail   34-42 (38) mm
          Forearm   31.0-35.6 mm
          Weight   3.8-7.7 g

Description: Reddish-brown dorsal fur with lighter brown on the ventral surface. Older animals sometimes lack the reddish tinge to their fur. The skin over the forearm is the same colour as that on the wing.

Habits: Nocturnal. Roosts in trees, often communally.

Habitat: Wide range of forest habitats.

Food: Insects collected from the top of the forest understorey.

Breeding: One young born in the late spring or early summer. Weaning is completed by mid February.

Distribution: Tasmania, Victoria, New South Wales, south eastern South Australia and southern West Australia.

Status: Wholly protected. Forests regenerated after logging operations are unlikely to provide as many suitable roosting sites as mature forests and this may lead to the long-term reduction of all Vespadelus species. Common at present.

Little Forest Vespadelus
(Formerly Eptesicus)

Vespadelus vulturnus

Order CHIROPTERA   Family Vespertilionidae
Size   Head & body   40-50 (44) mm
    Tail   30-40 (34) mm
    Forearm   27.2-31.7 mm
    Weight   3.7-5.6 g

Description: The smallest Tasmanian bat. Dorsal fur is mid dark-grey and ventral fur is grey with distinct pale tips. The tragus is often translucent white. The skin over the forearm is distinctly lighter than on the wing membrane.

Habits: Nocturnal. Roosts in trees often communally.

Habitat: Wide range of forest habitats but appears to favour lowland situations.

Food: Insects collected from the top of the forest understorey.

Breeding: One young born in late spring or early summer. Weaning is completed by mid February.

Distribution: Tasmania, Victoria, New South Wales, South Australia, Western Australia and Northern Territory.

Status: Wholly protected. Forests regenerated after logging operations are unlikely to provide as many suitable roosting sites as mature forests and this may lead to the long-term reduction of all Vespadelus species. Common at present.

Large Forest Vespadelus
(Formerly Eptesicus)

Vespadelus darlingtoni

Order CHIROPTERA   Family Vespertilionidae
Size   Head & body   40-60 (50) mm
          Tail   40 mm
          Forearm   32.0-37.0 mm
          Weight   4.8-7.8 g

Description: The previous two species of bats are very similar to the Large Forest Vespadelus. The main distinguishing features being the forearm length and the skin colour of the forearm and wing membrane. The Large Forest Vespadelus has dark-brown or almost black fur on its dorsal surface and is paler underneath. The skin over the forearm is the same colour as the wing membrane.

Habits: Nocturnal. Roosts in trees often communally.

Habitat: Wide range of forest habitats including rainforest.

Food: Insects collected from the middle layer of the forest between the canopy and understorey.

Breeding: One young born in late spring or early summer. Weaning is completed by mid-February.

Distribution: South eastern New South Wales, southern and eastern Victoria, north eastern Queensland and Tasmania.

Status: Wholly protected. Forests regenerated after logging operations are unlikely to provide as many suitable roosting sites as mature forests and this may lead to the long-term reduction of all Vespadelus species Common in available habitat.

77

Water Rat

Hydromys chrysogaster

Order Rodentia   Family Muridae
Size   Head & body   26 cm
         Tail   27 cm
         Weight   600 g

Description: The Water Rat has thick, glossy, water- repellent fur which is dark brown above and golden orange below. Thick tail which usually has a white tip. Small eyes, ears and nostrils which are set high on the head. Broad, partly webbed hind feet.

Habits: Nocturnal and crepuscular. Constructs tunnels in banks.

Habitat: Near permanent bodies of fresh or brackish water. Also estuaries and offshore island groups in salt water.

Food: Aquatic insects, fish, crustaceans. Also small mammals and water birds.

Breeding: Throughout the year, but mostly in spring and summer. Up to five litters may be produced annually, each litter has three to four young, which are suckled for one month and then remain with the mother for another month.

Distribution: Tasmania and all mainland states.

Status: Partly protected. Species considered secure. Common.

Long-tailed Mouse

Pseudomys higginsi

Order RODENTIA Family Muridae
Size Head & body 13 cm
     Tail   16 cm
     Weight   70 g

Description: Soft dark-grey fur above and paler underneath. Long tail is grey above and white below.

Habits: Mostly nocturnal, but may be seen in daylight, particularly in winter. Makes tunnels and runways beneath the forest debris.

Habitat: Most abundant in high rainfall areas of western Tasmania. Also found in wetter forests in eastern Tasmania and beneath screes in sub-alpine and alpine areas.

Food: Fungi, insects, spiders, seeds and fruit.

Breeding: Nests are built in decaying logs or stumps. Breeding occurs from late spring to late summer, and two litters, each of three to four young, may be reared in a good season. Young remain with mother until they reach maturity at age of three months.

Distribution: Endemic to Tasmania.

Status: Wholly protected. Appears secure in rainforest habitat and also able to recolonise clear-felled areas. Common in limited habitat.

New Holland Mouse

Pseudomys novaehollandiae

Order RODENTIA   Family Muridae
Size   Head & body   8 cm
          Tail   9 cm
          Weight   25 g

Description: Short thick grey-brown fur above with grey-white fur below. Tail brown above and white below. The New Holland Mouse may be distinguished from the introduced House Mouse (page 102) by its heavier build, its relatively larger eyes and ears, its more convex nose and hunched position when crouching. The lack of a notch in the upper incisor distinguishes this animal positively from a House Mouse.

Habits: Nocturnal.

Habitat: Dry heathlands and open sclerophyll forest in the north east of Tasmania on sandy soils.

Food: Seeds, insects, flowers, leaves and fungi.

Breeding: Nests in long burrows. Breeding occurs from early November to late March in Tasmania. Litter size varies from two to six. Young are weaned by about thirty days and may become sexually mature at seven weeks.

Distribution: North eastern Tasmania and Flinders Island, Victoria and New South Wales.

Status: Wholly protected. However, the species is vulnerable to clearing of its restricted heathland habitat and also to any change in the frequency of fire burning the heathland. Rare, although may increase after fires.

Broad-toothed Mouse
(Formerly Broad-toothed Rat)

Pseudomys fuscus

Order RODENTIA   Family Muridae
Size   Head & body   16 cm
        Tail   11 cm
        Weight   120 g

Description: Sandy to dark brown coloured fur above and paler below. General plump appearance. Broad round head and cheek pouches; small round ears and wide molar teeth that give it its common name.

Habits: Mostly nocturnal but can be seen during the day. Constructs runways under dense vegetation.

Habitat: High rainfall areas, including scrub, sedgeland and sub-alpine heathlands.

Food: Sedges, grasses, seeds. Also leaves and bark from shrubs.

Breeding: Well built nests are constructed under logs or in dense undergrowth. Breeds from early spring to mid-summer. Litter size varies from one to three young which are weaned at about five weeks. Females probably bear two litters per season.

Distribution: Tasmania, Victoria and south eastern New South Wales.

Status: Wholly protected. This species depends on areas of wet scrub, sedgeland, etc., which have been protected from fire for long periods. Over-frequent burning has led to the loss of much of its habitat. This species is regarded as potentially vulnerable. Uncommon.

Swamp Rat

Rattus lutreolus

Order RODENTIA   Family Muridae
Size   Head & body   16 cm
          Tail   11 cm
          Weight   120 g

Description: The Swamp Rat has soft thick dark grey-brown fur above and paler coloured fur underneath. Tail is dark grey and scaly. Small ears. May be distinguished from introduced rats (the Black Rat - page 98 and Brown Rat - page 100) by the fact that its tail is much shorter than its head and body and appears plumper.

Habits: Mainly nocturnal, but frequently seen during the day. Constructs tunnels through dense vegetation.

Habitat: Widespread across a range of habitats, including sedgeland, heathland and forest.

Food: Grasses, sedges, ferns, fungi and insects.

Breeding: Nests are constructed in burrows or grass tussocks. Breeds from early spring to autumn with three to five young born per litter. Young are independent after four weeks. Each adult female may have several litters per season.

Distribution: Tasmania, Victoria, eastern New South Wales, south eastern South Australia and Queensland.

Status: Wholly protected. The Swamp Rat is probably the most widespread and abundant species of native mammal in Tasmania. Abundant.

Australian Fur Seal

Arctocephalus pusillus doriferus

Order PINNIPEDIA   Family Otariidae
Size   Head & body   2 m
          Weight males   280 kg
          Weight females   80 kg

Description: Adult males are dark grey-brown above with a well developed mane of coarse lighter hair on neck and shoulders. When wet, males appear steely-grey. Adult females are ginger-brown to silver. This species has a blunter muzzle than Arctocephalus forsteri (page 90). Newborn pups are black. External ears small.

Habits: Forms dense colonies with territorial males and harems of females during the breeding season (November to December). Superb swimmers (as are all seals) which can dive to at least 120m.

Habitat: Rocky islands and exposed reefs. Coastal seas and extending over the continental shelf.

Food: Cephalopods and fish, mainly schooling fish such as Redbait and Jack Mackerel. Also reef fish such as Leather-jackets.

Breeding: Dense colonies occur during the breeding season. Pupping sites are dominated by large males which defend territories aggressively. Pups are born during November/ December. One pup born per female. Pups are suckled for about eight months. Approximately two percent of pups continue to suckle into their second and third year.

Distribution: Coasts and seas of Victoria, New South Wales and Tasmania. Abundant in Bass Strait.

Status: Common. Total population between 35 000 to 45 000 Wholly protected.

● Breeding sites

New Zealand Fur Seal

Arctocephalus forsteri

Order PINNIPEDIA   Family Otariidae
Size   Head & body   2 m
         Weight males   160 kg
         Weight females   70 kg

Description: Adults dark grey-brown above, lighter grey-brown below. Males have a well developed mane of longer hair. Muzzle is sharply pointed. External ears small. Newborn pups are black.

Habits: Forms colonies with territorial males and harems of females during the breeding season (October to December).

Habitat: Exposed rocky coasts and islands. Coastal seas and extending over the continental shelf.

Food: Fish, cephalopods and birds such as Short-tailed Shearwaters and Fairy Penguins.

Breeding: Colonies form during the breeding season. Breeding seals choose beaches with large boulders to give protection for pupping. These traditional sites are dominated by large males which defend territories aggressively. Pups are born from November to January. Pups are weaned at about eight months. During winter (July to August) the pups congregate in groups. About fifty pups are born each year in southern Tasmania.

Distribution: Coasts and seas of southern Western Australia, South Australia, south coast of Tasmania and New Zealand. Also Macquarie, Snares, Auckland, Campbell, Bounty and Chatham Islands.

Status: Common globally although rare in Tasmania. Wholly protected.

● Breeding site

Southern Elephant Seal

Mirounga leonina

Order PINNIPEDIA Family Phocidae
Size Head & body males 4 m
      Head & body females 2.5 m
      Weight males 3000 kg
      Weight females 300 kg

Description: Males are huge and dark-grey to greyish-brown in colour. Neck region is frequently heavily scarred and cracked. Males have large inflatable proboscis. Females are browner and generally darker than males. Both sexes have a heavily built body with short hair and no external ears.

Habits: Adults come ashore during late August to September. Females form harems within the territory of a breeding male. Adults return to land for the annual moult which is mainly from December to January. Moult lasts about six weeks. Large gatherings are only found on shore during the breeding season and the moult. Recorded diving up to 1600 m with dives lasting up to 2 hours.

Habitat: Islands, coastal seas and the southern ocean.

Food: Cephalopods and fish.

Breeding: Large colonies form during the breeding season (September to November). Dominant males preside over harems of about twenty to forty females. Most pups are born in October and suckled for about three weeks. After weaning the pups gather in groups for about two weeks before heading to sea. Most females produce about seven pups during their lifetime.

Distribution: Circumpolar. Found throughout the southern oceans and on most sub-Antarctic islands. A breeding colony once existed on King Island in Bass Strait. This colony was hunted to extinction during the early 19th century. Occasional animals are found on the Tasmanian coast. They are regularly found on Maatsuyker Island where they have bred at least three times in the last 20 years.

Status: Abundant globally but rare in Tasmania. Wholly protected.

● Breeding site

Leopard Seal

Hydrurga leptonyx

Order PINNIPEDIA   Family Phocidae
Size   Head & body males   3 m
        Head & body females   3.5 m
        Weight males   260 kg
        Weight females   400 kg

Description: Long slim body with 'reptilian' looking large head. Adults dark-grey above, lighter grey below with light and dark-grey spots on the throat, shoulders and sides. Jaws have a wide gape.

Habits: Solitary. Hauls out on ice floes to rest. Lies in wait near penguin colonies to prey on penguins that enter the water.

Habitat: Northern fringes of Antarctic pack-ice and adjacent oceans with regular dispersal into more temperate waters.

Food: The Leopard Seal is a major predator of seals and penguins such as King, Adelie, Gentoo and Macaroni. Also eats cephalopods, fish, carrion and large amounts of krill.

Breeding: Extended breeding season. Pups are born from September to January. Weaning probably about four weeks.

Distribution: Circumpolar. Ranging north from the pack-ice to many sub-Antarctic islands such as South Georgia, Kerguelen, Heard, St Paul and Macquarie. Leopard Seals regularly disperse to the coasts of New Zealand, southern Australia and Tasmania with a seasonal peak during August/September. These dispersing seals are mainly immature animals.

Status: Common globally although rare in Tasmania. Wholly protected.

Introduced Mammals

Black Rat

Rattus rattus

Order RODENTIA		Family Muridae
Size	Head & body	19 cm
	Tail	23 cm
	Weight	280 g

Description: Brown-black to light-brown fur. Sleek elongated body. Large ears, eyes and a pointed snout. Has larger ears, more slender hind-feet and longer tail than the Brown Rat.

Habits: Mainly nocturnal. Good swimmer and climber. Has a fondness for wall cavities and roofs. A timid animal.

Habitat: Widespread, particularly near watercourses, farms, rubbish dumps and warehouses.

Food: Omnivorous.

Breeding: Nests are constructed of any fibrous material. Breeds continuously and females may have six litters of five to ten young each year. Young are weaned at about twenty days.

Distribution: Tasmania and all mainland states.

Status: Introduced. Not protected. Abundant.

©Terry Pie

©Terry Pie

99

Brown Rat

Rattus norvegicus

Order RODENTIA   Family Muridae
Size   Head & body   24 cm
           Tail   20 cm
           Weight   320 g

Description: The Brown Rat has grey-brown fur above and is paler coloured underneath. It has a solid build and rather scruffy appearance. Small ears, eyes and a blunt snout.

Habits: Nocturnal. It is known for its aggressive nature and will attack when cornered, unlike the Black Rat and native rats which are timid.

Habitat: Found mainly in coastal and long established urban areas.

Food: Omnivorous.

Breeding: Nests in deep and extensive communal burrows. Breeds continuously throughout the year. Litters number from seven to ten young which are weaned when twenty days old.

Distribution: Tasmania, Victoria, southern New South Wales, southern Queensland and southern Western Australia.

Status: Introduced. Not protected. Common.

©Greg Fyfe

House Mouse

Mus musculus

Order RODENTIA   Family Muridae
Size   Head & body   7.5 cm
          Tail   8 cm
          Weight   20 g

Description: Brown or yellow-grey fur above and pale-grey to pale-yellow below. May be distinguished from the native New Holland Mouse by its more concave nose, relatively smaller ears and eyes and more elongated stance. Closer examination will show a notch on the inner surface of the House Mouse's upper incisors. The New Holland Mouse has no such notch.

Habits: Mainly nocturnal.

Habitat: Most common near human habitation, but also widespread in native vegetation, particularly that which has been recently burnt.

Food: Omnivorous but predominantly plants and seeds.

Breeding: Nests are built in burrows or crevices in buildings. Breeds continuously throughout the year. Four to eight young are born per litter. Young are usually sexually mature at eight weeks.

Distribution: Tasmania and all mainland states.

Status: Introduced. Not protected. Widespread and abundant.

European Fox

Vulpes vulpes

Order CARNIVORA   Family Canidae
Size   Head & body   55 - 85 cm
           Tail   32 - 45 cm
           Weight   4.5 - 9 kg

Description: Coat is usually a rich reddish brown but can vary from grey to sandy beige. The jaws, chin, throat and belly are white. Erect ears are pointed with black backs. Legs shortish, lower legs and feet usually black. Tail is long, thick and bushy often with a white tip. At night Foxes show a bright, golden yellow eye-shine. The dog (male) is usually larger than the vixen (female).

Habits: Usually nocturnal and crepuscular but may be seen in daylight. When hunted Foxes become very secretive. They rest by day in an earth (den) or hollow log, in thick vegetation or under a shed.

Habitat: Found in a wide range of habitats from forests and agricultural land to alpine country and even urban areas.

Food: Although the Fox is a carnivore it is an opportunistic predator and scavenger. It eats whatever it can find including rabbits, small wallabies, bandicoots, mice, reptiles, birds, nests and earthworms. Preys on farm livestock such as lambs and hens. Fond of blackberries, apples and other fruit. Surplus food is cached.

Breeding: Mating is during the winter with 4 – 5 cubs born in the earth during spring. Cubs are dark brown at first and emerge from the earth from 4 weeks. The vixens scream normally during winter mating season.

Distribution: The most widespread, abundant wild carnivore in the world. Introduced to Australia where it has caused severe declines and extinctions of several native species. Recently introduced to Tasmania by persons unknown.

Status: Widespread on mainland Australia. Remains rare in Tasmania and is subject to an intense eradication campaign.

Appendix 1

FOOTPRINTS

Ibfromation courtesy of Parks & Wildlife Service

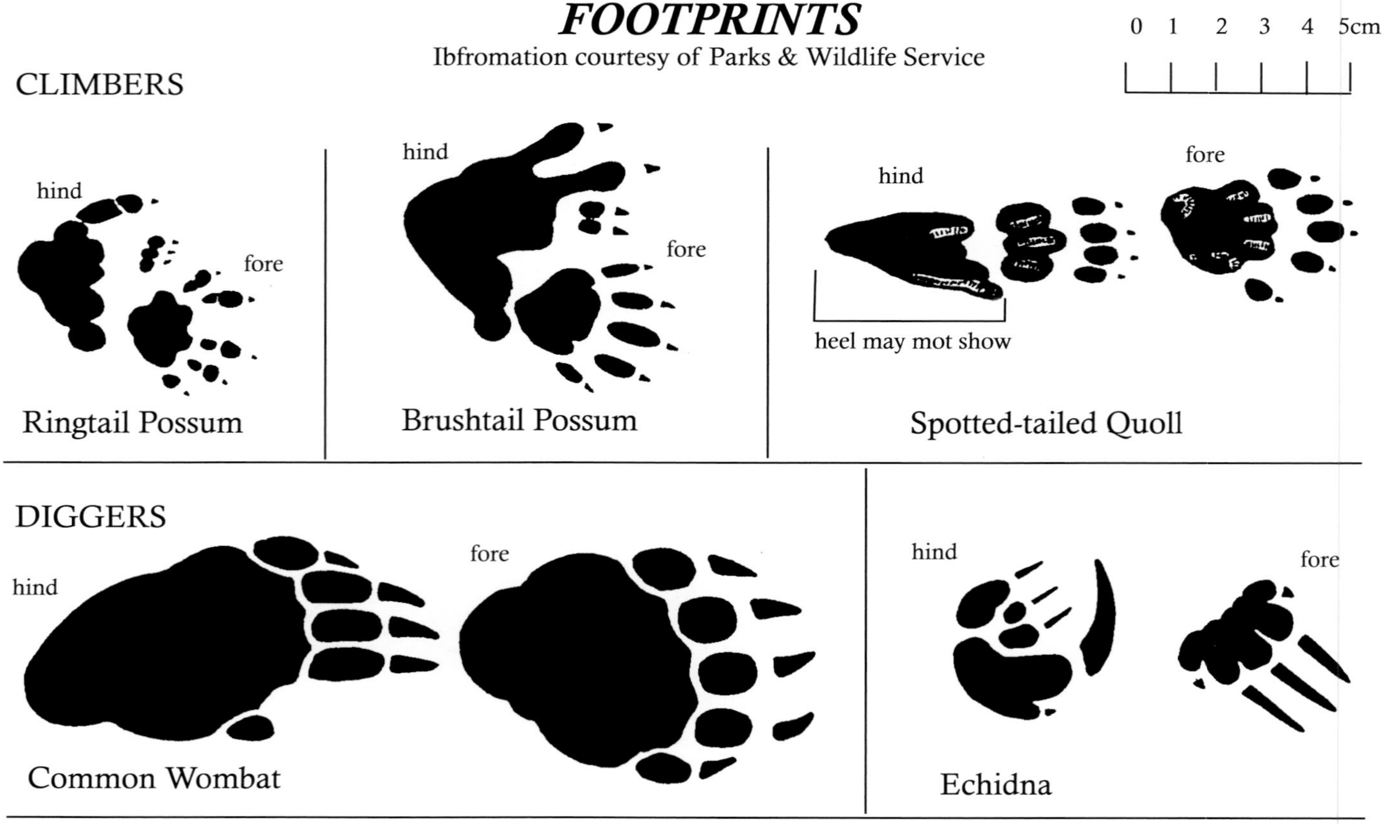

0 1 2 3 4 5cm
CLIMBERS
hind
fore
Ringtail Possum
hind
fore
Brushtail Possum
hind
fore
heel may mot show
Spotted-tailed Quoll
DIGGERS
hind
fore
Common Wombat
hind
fore
Echidna

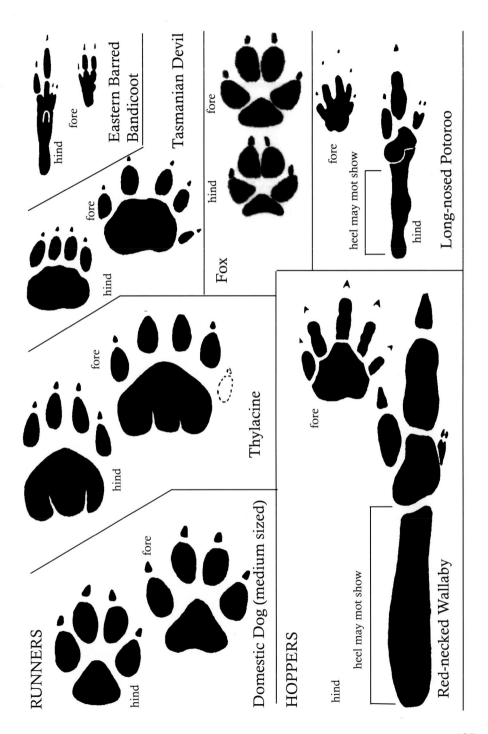

RUNNERS

Eastern Barred Bandicoot
hind   fore

Tasmanian Devil
fore   hind

fore   hind

Long-nosed Potoroo
fore   hind
heel may mot show

Fox
fore   hind

Thylacine
fore   hind

Domestic Dog (medium sized)
fore   hind

HOPPERS

fore

hind
heel may mot show

Red-necked Wallaby

Appendix 11 - Where to see Tasmanian mammals in National Parks

KEY

★ Present
○ Absent
☆ Unconfirmed

	Walls of Jerusalem	Strezlecki	South-West	Rocky Cape	Mount William	Mount Field	Maria Island	Hartz Mountains	Freycinet	Franklin-lower Gordon	Cradle Mt Lake St Clair	Ben Lomond	Narawntapu	Douglas/Apsley
Platypus	★	○	★			★	○			★	★	★	★	★
Echidna	★	★	★	★	★	★	★	★	★	★	★	★	★	★
Spotted-tailed Quoll	★	○	★	★	★	★	○	★	★	★	★	★		★
Eastern Quoll	★	○	★	★	★	★	○	★	★	★	★	★	★	★
Tasmann Devil	★	○	★	★	★	★	○	★	★	★	★		★	★
Dusky Antechinus			★						★	★	★			★
Swamp Antechinus		★	★		★		★		★	★	★	★	☆	
White-footed Dunnart					★	☆	☆		★	☆	☆	☆		★
Thylacine	☆	○	☆	○	☆		○	☆	○	★	○		○	
Southern Brown Bandicoot		★	★		★		★		★	○	★	★	★	★
Eastern Barred Bandicoot	○		○				★			★			★	★
Common Wombat		★	★	★	★	★	★	★	★	★	★	★	★	★
Common Ringtail Possum	★	★	★	★	★	★	○	★	★	★	★	★	★	★
Sugar Glider		★	★						★	★				★
Common Brushtail Possum	★	★	★	★	★	★	★	★	★	★	★	★	★	★

Species	1	2	3	4	5	6	7	8	9	10	11	12	13
Eastern Pygmy Possum	★				★	★		★				☆	★
Little Pygmy Possum	★		★		★	☆		★			☆		★
Long-nosed Potoroo	★				★	★	★	★			★	★	
Tasmanian Bettong	★	☆		○		★	★	★	○		★	○	☆
Tasmanian Pademelon	★	★	★	★	★	★	★	★	★	★	★	★	★
Red-necked Wallaby	★	★	★	★	★	★	★	★	★	★	★	★	★
Eastern Grey Kangaroo	★	★	○	○	○	○	○	○	○		○	○	○
Greater Long-eared Bat			★			★	☆	☆	★				
Lesser Long-eared Bat			★	★	★	★	☆	☆	☆	☆	★	★	☆
Gould's Wattled Bat						★	☆	☆	☆				
Chocolated Wattled Bat			★	★	★	★	☆	☆	★	★	☆	☆	☆
Tasmanian Pipistrelle				★	★	★	☆	☆	★			★	★
Little Forest Vespadelus	☆		★	★	★	★	☆	☆	★	★	☆	☆	☆
King River Vespadelus			★	★	★	★	☆	☆	★	★	☆	★	☆
Large Forest Vespadelus	☆		☆	★	★	★	☆	☆		★	☆	☆	
Water Rat	★				★	★	★	★	★	★	★	★	
Long-tailed Mouse	★	★	★	★	★	★	★				★	★	★
New Holland Mouse				★			○	★					
Broad-toothed Mouse			★	★		★	○	★	★		★	★	
Swamp Rat	★		★	★	★	★	★	★	★	★	★	★	★
Black Rat	★		★	★	★	★	★	○	★		★	★	★
Brown Rat				★		★	★	○			☆		
House Mouse	★		★	★	★	★	★	★	★	★	★	★	★

Appendix 111

BATS

Information courtesy RJ Tayor, NG O'Neil & T Reardon

Chalinolobus   Vespadelus   Nyctophilus

Profiles showing the facial features
of the four genera of Tasmanian bats

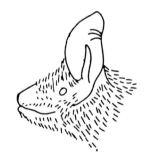

Falsistrellus

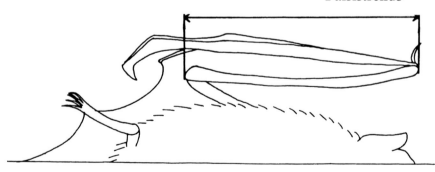

Diagram showing method of measuring forearm length

Useful Addresses with contact details

Parks and Wildlife Service Tasmania
GPO Box 1751
Hobart 7001
Phone: 1300 135 513
Web:www.parks.tas.gov.au

Please report any Fox sightings to the 24 hour Hotline:
1300 FOX OUT
1300 369 688

Please report any whale strandings/sightings to: 0427 Whales 0427 942537

Please report any Tasmanian Devils with DFTD to: 6233 6556

Tourism Tasmania
GPO Box 399
Hobart 7001
Phone: 61 3 6230 8235
Email: reception@tourism.tas.gov.au
Web:www.discovertasmania.com
        www.tastravel.com.au

Tasmanian Conservation Trust
102 Bathurst St
Hobart 7000
Phone: 61 3 6234 3552
Email: tct@southcom.com.au

Wilderness Society
GPO Box 716,
Hobart TAS 7001,
Phone: 61 3 6270 1701
Web: www.wilderness.org.au

GLOSSARY

Arboreal	-	living in a tree
Brackish	-	slightly salty
Carnivorous	-	feeding on animal flesh
Carrion	-	dead and putrefying flesh
Cephalopods	-	kinds of molluscs, including octopus, squid and cuttle-fish
Crepuscular	-	active mainly at dawn and dusk
Dimorphic	-	occurs in two colour forms
Diurnal	-	active during the day
Endemic	-	found in only one region
Invertebrate	-	an animal without a backbone
Nocturnal	-	active during the night
Noseleaf	-	a projecting structure on a bat's nose to direct ultra-sonic sounds uttered through the nostrils
Omnivorous	-	feeding on both animal and plant matter
Prehensile	-	being able to grip; normally applied to the tail
Sclerophyll	-	plants with hard or stiff leaves
Scree	-	rock debris on the slopes or at the base of hills
Sub-alpine	-	the zone between montane level and tree line
Torpor	-	breathing slows, body temperature falls and the animal does not respond to normal stimuli
Tragus	-	a flap situated inside the outer ear
Venomous	-	poisonous

BIBLIOGRAPHY AND RECOMMENDED READING LIST

THE MAMMALS OF TASMANIA by R H Green (1973), published by the Author, Launceston, Tasmania.

AUSTRALIAN MAMMALS: A FIELD GUIDE FOR NSW, VIC, SA, &: TAS by] Hyett & N Shaw (1980), published by Thomas Nelson Australia, Melbourne.

THE TASMANIAN TIGER by S Smith (1980), published by Tasmanian NP & WS.

THE MAMMALS of AUSTRALIA, edited by R. Strahan (1995) published by Reed Books.

TASMANIAN BATS: IDENTIFICATION, DISTRIBUTION &: NATURAL HISTORY by R] Taylor, M G O'Neil & T Reardon.
Papers and Proceedings of the Royal Society of Tasmania, Volume 121 (1987).

MAMMAL TRACKS &: SIGNS by B Triggs (1984), published by Oxford University Press, Australia.

RODENTS OF AUSTRALIA by C H S Watts & H] Aglin (1981), published by Angus & Robertson, Australian Natural Science Library.

DISTRIBUTION RECORDS OF NATIVE TERRESTRIAL MAMMALS IN TASMANIA (1991) by DE Rounsevell, R] Taylor and G] Hocking. Wildlife Research 18: 699-717.

NATIVE VERTEBRATES WHICH ARE RARE OR THREATENED IN TASMANIA (1994), Parks & Wildlife Service, Tasmania.

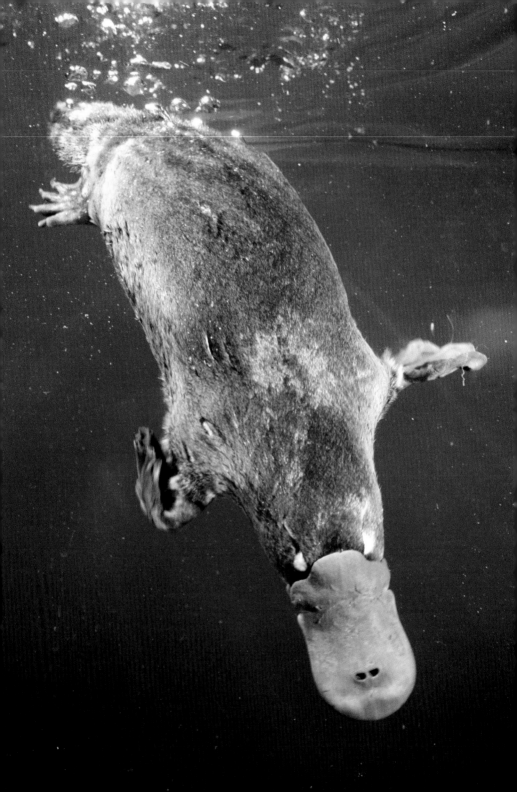

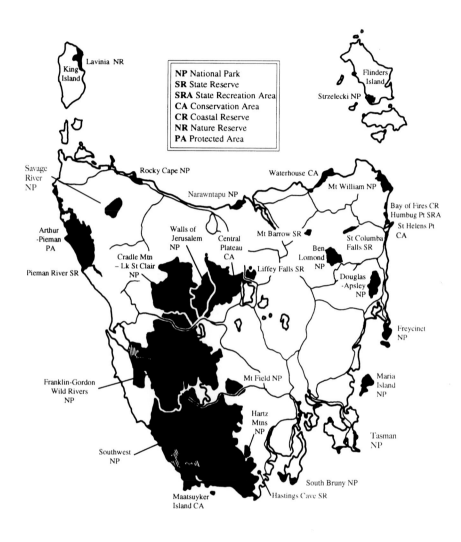

Map courtesy of The Tasmanian Parks & Wildlife Service

Opposite: Platypus diving

INDEX

Antechinus minimus 28
Antechinus swainsonii 26
Arctocephalus forsteri 90
Arctocephalus pusillus 88
Australian Fur Seal................ 88

Bennett's Wallaby 56
Bettongia gaimardi 52
Black Rat............................ 98
Broad-toothed Mouse............ 84
Brown Rat 100

Cercartetus lepidus. 48
Cercartetus nanus 46
Chalinolobus gouldii 66
Chalinolobus moria.................. 68
Chocolate Wattled Bat 68
Common Brushtail Possum ... 44
Common Ringtail Possum...... 40
Common Wombat. 38

Dasyurus maculatus.................. 20
Dasyurus viverrinus 22
Dusky Antechinus................. 26
Dusky Marsupial Mouse 26
Eastern Barred Bandicoot 36
European Fox 104

Eastern Grey Kangaroo 58
Eastern Pygmy-possum 46
Eastern Quoll 22
Echidna 16

Falsistrellus tasmaniensis 70
Forester Kangaroo 58

Gould's Wattled Bat. 66
Greater Long-eared Bat 62

House Mouse 102
Hydromys chrysogaster 78
Hydrurga leptonyx................... 94

Isoodon obesulus 34

King River Vespadelus........... 72

Large Forest Vespadelus 76
Leopard Seal.... 94
Lesser Long-eared Bat........... 64
Little Forest Vespadelus 74
Little Marsupial Mouse......... 28
Little Pygmy-possum............. 48
Long-nosed Potoroo 50
Long-tailed Mouse............... 80

Macropus giganteus.................. 58
Macropus rufogriseus............... 56
Mirounga leonina 92
Mus musculus 102

Native Cat 22
New Holland Mouse............. 82
New Zealand Fur Seal.......... 90
Nyctophilus geoffroyi 64
Nyctophilus timoriensis 62

Omithorhynchus anatinus 14

Perameles gunnii 36
Petaurus breviceps 42
Platypus 14
Potorous tridactylus.................. 50
Pseudomys fuscus 84
Pseudomys higginsi 80
Pseudomys novaehollandiae 82
Pseudocheirus peregrinus 40

Rattus lutreolus 86
Rattus norvegicus 100
Rattus rattus *98*
Red-necked Wallaby .... .56
Ringtail Possum 40

Sarcophilus harrisii 24
Sminthopsis leucopus 30
Southern Brown Bandicoot .. .34
Southern Elephant Seal 92
Spotted-tailed Quoll 20
Sugar Glider 42
Swamp Antechinus 28
Swamp Rat 86

Tachyglossus aculeatus 16
Tasmanian Bettong 52
Tasmanian Devil 24
Tasmanian Tiger 32
Tasmanian Pademelon .... .54
Tasmanian Pipistrelle 70
Thylacine 32
Thylacinus cynocephalus 32
Thylogale billardierii 54
Tiger Cat 20
Trichosurus vulpecula 44

Vespadelus darlingtoni. 76
Vespadelus regulus 72
Vespadelus vulturnus 74
Vombatus ursinus 38
Vulpes vulpes 104

Water Rat. 78
White-footed Dunnart 30
Wombat 38

Over: Tasmanian Devil